FRANK D. DRAKE

Associate Astronomer

National Radio Astronomy Observatory

Intelligent Life in Space

ILLUSTRATED

with photographs and diagrams

THE MACMILLAN COMPANY New York

MACMILLAN NEW YORK London

To STEVE and RIP

Contents

List of Illustrations

Introduction

F O R thousands of years, men have been looking at the dazzling spectacle of the night sky and been wondering what all the bright points of light might look like if they could be seen up close. How did they come to be there? What did they look like in the past? What will they look like in the future? The invention of the telescope has allowed us to answer many of these questions. We know now that the brightest object we see, the moon, is a small barren body that goes around the earth following a nearly circular path called an orbit. The points of light that seem to wander among the stars are planets ("planet" means "wanderer" in Greek). These, like our own planet, the earth, orbit around our star, the sun. We also know that all stars are objects like our sun. Some are larger or smaller, hotter or cooler, to be sure, but they are still objects of which our sun is a very average example.

In finding these answers to some of mankind's basic questions about the sky, or space, as it is now called, new and often more difficult questions have been raised. Have all the stars existed forever, or are some younger than others? Is our sun one of the oldest or one of the youngest objects in space? Do other stars carry with them planets like those in our own solar system? If the answer to this is "yes," perhaps the most fascinating question of all arises: Are there other people in space?

The ideal way to answer these last two questions would be to build a telescope large enough to look at some nearby stars to see if they have inhabited planets, but the distance to the nearest stars is so great that no imaginable telescope could succeed at this task. Instead, the answers must be found in a roundabout way. It is first necessary to understand how the objects in our universe have originated and what they are made of, especially stars, planets, and living things. Then, when this is known, the human mind can calculate how many stars could support intelligent beings, even though we cannot actually see whether they are there.

Introduction

Science is now able to supply some answers that, considered together, can tell us something about other civilizations in space. It seems quite certain that not only a few, but countless civilizations have been born, and perhaps died, during the course of time. Now, we would very much like to talk to one of these civilizations. This conversation would prove the conclusions about the possibility of other intelligent life. Our technology provides several ways in which we might do this, but some seem better than others.

In the following chapters there will be a description of the facts that seem to point to the existence of many civilizations in space and the ways in which we might contact such civilizations. These facts have been found by using telescopes that, though large and well made, can grasp only a fraction of the grandeur of the universe. Thus, some of the facts may be incomplete, and some of the conclusions not exactly correct. In any case, it is hoped that the reader will learn a great many things about space that he did not know before. If some ideas here are wrong, it will be the task of scientists to find the correct answers during the years to come. In science, the answers are always there to be found. Only sufficient skill and determination are needed to find a path of research leading to them.

Frank D. Drake

Galileo's telescope.

CHAPTER ONE

Our Real Home

WHERE did mankind come from? Where is our real birthplace? Throughout most of history, learned men have thought that the earth was the most important object in space —in fact, the center of the universe. In 1610, however, Galileo Galilei, one of the great early astronomers, turned the first telescope to the sky from his home in Italy and discovered that this idea seemed wrong. The astronomers who followed him proved Galileo correct and replaced the old idea about the earth with a much more exciting picture of space. It was soon realized that the earth was not the center of things, but only a minor planet of the sun. Then it was found that even the sun was not at the center of the universe, but orbited through space with a separate group of 100 billion stars. One hundred billion stars is more than any of us can imagine, more than the grains of sand on a beach. Such a large separate group of orbiting stars is called a galaxy.

Every star we see in the sky belongs to our galaxy. Surprisingly, these stars are arranged in a shape resembling a very flat pancake, and the sun is located out toward its edge. We see some of this vast disk of stars as the great band of light in the night sky called the Milky Way, although it is only through a telescope that the band can be seen to be made of countless separate stars. A çareful look at this band of light on a clear dark night will show that it is blotchy. In places its gleam seems to be covered by clouds of dust. This illusion is close to the truth. Orbiting in space along with the stars are great clouds of dust and gases, called nebulae, that, as will be seen, actually are very important to our galaxy. The dust of space is not black, but rather a gray color, as can be seen from the photograph of the nebula near Merope, one of the Pleiades, a star cluster in the constellation Taurus, the Bull. In the photograph, the nebula is reflecting the light of Merope. These dust clouds are something of a nuisance when we try to look at our galaxy, because they are

The nebula near the star Merope.

so thick that they hide all but about one-tenth of the Milky Way from our telescopes. That is, except from the telescopes that observe radio waves rather than light waves, the radio telescopes that are able to penetrate through dust clouds. It is unfortunate that the center of our galaxy, the most exciting part of all, is hidden by the dust clouds in the constellation Sagittarius, the Archer.

Star clouds in the constellation Sagittarius.

As we turn our attention to distances far beyond the Milky Way, we find that the universe contains many other galaxies, islands of stars floating through the vast empty seas of space. There are perhaps 100 million ✓ galaxies, each with 100 billion stars. By multiplying these figures, it appears that the total amount of stars in space is the enormous number expressed by writing a 1 with 20 zeros after it, more than all the grains of sand on all the beaches of the earth. The Great Nebula in the constellation Andromeda, named for the character in Greek mythology, is one of the galaxies nearest to our own. It is also the most distant celestial object that can be seen without the telescope, and a twin to our own galaxy. If the photograph of the Great Nebula were of the Milky Way, the solar system would be located in the edge of the visible rim.

However, when one considers the history of the sun and the earth, and other civilizations that might be contacted in space, it is only our galaxy that matters. The other galaxies of stars are too far away, and have never had an important influence on our own. It is the Milky Way that has given birth to our solar system and to the only other planetary systems that may be within reach of radio and space probes. All the stars in the sky have originated in those great dust clouds that are seen faintly against the sweep of the Milky Way, for the dust of space, the cosmic dust, is ✓ the material from which stars and planets are made.

The Great Nebula in the constellation Andromeda.

When stars grow old, as indeed they do, they return some of their material to space. There it rejoins the dust clouds, sometimes to make new stars again. Everything on the earth—ourselves, the trees, the oceans, even the knobs on our TV sets—was once dust in space, and before that, gas somewhere in the heart of a star. Our real home, the place from which our earth has come, is the Milky Way.

Sometimes it seems as though nothing changes in the sky, except for the positions of the planets and the moon among the stars. This is almost right. Over the course of a year, or even 50 years, most of the changes among the stars can be found only through very careful measurements with large telescopes; but if we look very closely, we can see with our own eyes a few stars that do change. For instance, Algol, the second brightest star in the constellation of Perseus, sometimes glows with only half its usual brightness for an interval of several hours. This winking repeats as regularly as clockwork, approximately every 2 days and 21 hours. Some astronomical magazines, such as *Sky and Telescope,* list the times when Algol becomes fainter.

It would be a mistake, however, to decide nothing much is happening in the Milky Way just because most changes occur slowly. The speed at which *we* do things is not necessarily the speed of the stars. Just because we sleep, have three meals, and change our clothes every 24 hours, or go from winter to summer in just six months, doesn't mean that *everything* in the universe should make important changes so rapidly. The Milky Way changes, too, in its own time.

Because of the great size of the stars of the Milky Way, and of the galaxy itself, changes take a very long time. Just as large plants and animals change much more slowly than small ones, so the Milky Way makes its important changes very slowly in comparison to the rate at which things change on the earth. Astronomers often measure time in the Milky Way not by earth years, but by the "cosmic year," the time it takes for the stars to make one revolution about the center of our galaxy. This is about 200 million earth years.

Stars do not remain in the same position forever, as the figures of the Big Dipper as it appeared about 50 thousand years ago, appears at the present, and will appear about 50 thousand years from now, show. Because of the enormous distances separating us from these stars, their great velocities result in relatively small angular changes of their observed positions, but it is possible to determine how our sky looked in the past and how it will look in the future. The sun and our solar system, if viewed from nearby stars, would be seen to move across the sky at an average speed of about 42 thousand miles per hour. Nevertheless, because of the great distances involved, the motion would be almost imperceptible. Stars also change in appearance and structure as they age.

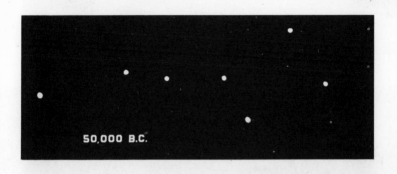

50,000 B.C.

PRESENT TIME

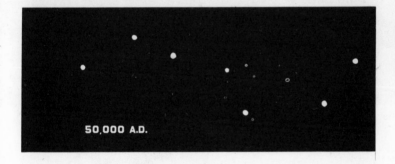

50,000 A.D.

The changing form of the Big Dipper.

*Globular star cluster, one of the oldest
groups of stars in our galaxy,
in the constellation Hercules.*

The lifetimes of typical stars such as the sun are about 50 cosmic years. After they reach that age, they change into faint stars called white dwarfs. These are tiny, feeble bodies in which the material is so closely packed together that a matchboxful may weigh a ton. So the cosmic year, as long as it is, has approximately the same meaning to a star as our year has to us. It is very important, when thinking about what is happening to the stars, to consider what happens over *cosmic years*, rather than over earth years. When we do this, we begin to see our galaxy as it really is: a bustling, changing place, where every cosmic year brings something new and exciting.

Like men on the earth, new stars are always being born and old stars dying. There are even families, or clusters, of stars that travel together through the vastness of space. The matter thrown off from an older generation of stars becomes gas and dust and goes to make up a new generation. These new stars will be different from the old generation because of continual changes in the scrap material.

How does all this come about? Astronomers now think that our galaxy was born perhaps 20 billion years (or 100 cosmic years) ago as a great swirling cloud of hydrogen gas. Hydrogen is the simplest of the many basic chemical elements from which everything is made. About 70 per cent of everything in space is hydrogen; the remainder is mainly helium, the next most simple element. This amount of hydrogen is not present on the earth, however, for reasons to be discussed later. From this great cloud of hydrogen, stars were formed, generating their light as a result of nuclear reactions taking place near their centers. These nuclear reactions are closely related to those often mentioned in the newspapers in connection with new atomic electrical powerplants and defense weapons. In the reactions that take place in stars, hydrogen is changed into helium by the joining together of many nuclei of the simple hydrogen atoms. In this process the energy, or heat, that is produced eventually appears at the surface of the star, as very bright light, as it does in our sun. But this cannot go on forever, because eventually most of the hydrogen in the center of a star is exhausted.

What does the star do then? One might expect it to get cold, to stop shining, as the terrific heat generated in its center fades away. As the pressure in the star, or the outward push of the gases, becomes smaller, one would expect the star to collapse into a small, cold body. But strangely enough, the star does just the opposite. It begins to collapse as the heat dies, but this action itself compresses the very center of the star, causing this region to become even hotter. This same process occurs when one operates a bicycle pump. In this case, as the bicycle pump is used, the air inside it is heated as it is compressed by the pumping action.

The warmer air makes the whole pump hotter, as one can discover by touching it. Inside the star, the center finally gets so hot that new nuclear reactions begin in which helium is converted to still more complicated elements. The total production of heat actually increases, and the star gets brighter. In fact, it swells up as a result of all these changes, and becomes a giant or supergiant star. Many of these stars are very red in color, as well as being very bright. Examples we can see are the star Betelgeuse in the shoulder of Orion, the Hunter; Arcturus, which is the brightest star in the constellation Boötes, the Bear Driver, and is pointed to by the end of the handle of the Big Dipper; and Antares in the constellation of Scorpio, the Scorpion. Some of these stars are enormous. For instance, if either Betelgeuse or Antares were the same distance from the earth as the sun is, we would be deep within the star.

This giant stage lasts only a relatively short time. After the star has finally used up most of the possible ways to make heat-energy from nuclear reactions, it begins to collapse into a white-dwarf star. In this state it will carry out the conversion of its little remaining hydrogen into helium, giving forth a little heat and a very feeble light for hundreds of cosmic years more.

It is during the giant stage of a star's life, and the collapse to the white-dwarf state, that events very important to the eventual appearance of living things in space occur. Astronomers have now turned their telescopes on many stars going through these final steps in their development. They have found that these stars are throwing some of their material into space in many ways. Some stars do it slowly, so that the material thrown off is nearly invisible. Others cast forth

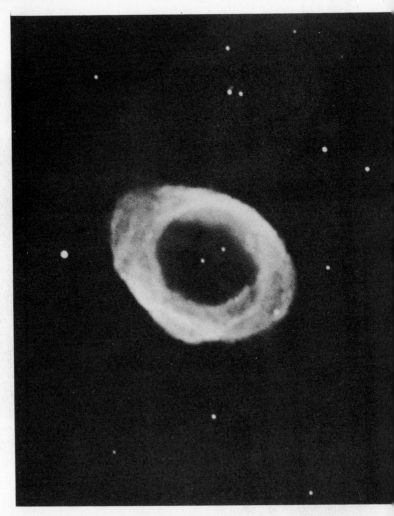

The "Ring" Nebula, a planetary nebula in the constellation Lyra, the Lyre.

the material a little more quickly, over periods of thousands of years, after which they are surrounded by glowing clouds of the gas they have thrown off; we call these planetary nebulae. Still other stars do it in a more spectacular way, by exploding violently in times as short as a day. Such an exploding star, which is called a nova, may get 50 thousand times brighter as it throws part of itself into space, and it may take months before the brightness returns to normal. The photograph of Nova Persei shows the material thrown off in a nova explosion that occurred in the constellation Perseus in the year 1901; the star that exploded is still visible.

Expanding nebulosity around Nova Persei.

Every once in a while an even more violent explosion occurs in which the brightness of the star increases nearly 100 million times. This explosion, perhaps the most spectacular event in the universe, is called a supernova explosion. When a supernova is at its brightest, it is sometimes brighter than all the other 10 billion or so stars in its galaxy combined. A supernova also takes many months to return to its normal brightness.

These great phenomena do not occur very often. We

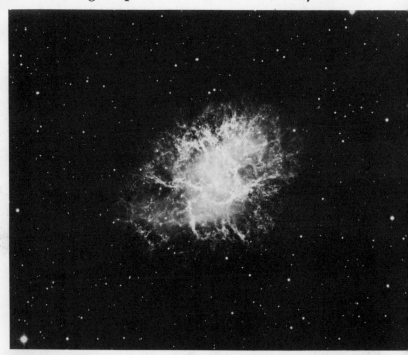

The Crab Nebula.

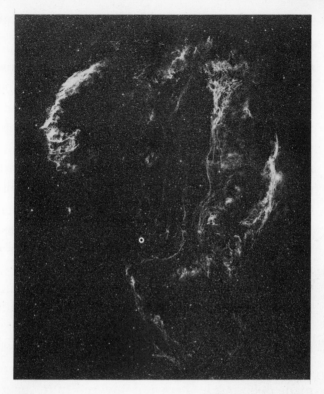

The Cygnus Loop.

have seen them in our Milky Way during the last thousand years only in 1054, 1572, and 1604. However, we can now use our optical and radio telescopes to see the great clouds of gas thrown off by old supernova explosions. Even today, 900 years later, the gas from the supernova of 1054, the Crab Nebula in the constellation Taurus, is brightly shining and exploding outward at a speed of over two million miles per hour. The filamentary nebula in the photograph of the Loop in the constellation Cygnus, the Swan, is the remains of a very old supernova explosion that occurred perhaps 50 thousand years ago, and astronomers are no longer able to find the star that exploded. The shell of material thrown off, which is seen in the photograph, is still moving outward at speeds of about 100 thousand miles per hour. It is heated and caused to glow visibly as it collides with the gas in space.

The material the stars are giving back to space is important because it contains the new complex chemical elements built in the fiery nuclear processes of the stars. Living things can be made only from such elements. All known organisms are very complicated organizations of atoms based on the element carbon, particularly, but also on such elements as phosphorus and nitrogen. It is these essential elements the stars have made deep inside them and now return to space. New stars formed from interstellar material will consist not only of hydrogen, but the newly formed elements as well. These new stars will then have the ingredients that can make planets, and in turn, if the conditions are right, living things.

Astronomers can attach special instruments to their telescopes called spectrographs that can analyse elements in a star. A "spectrograph" is an instrument using prisms or similar devices to separate the light from a star into the many colors present in that light,

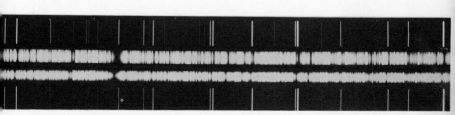

*Spectra of the constant velocity star Arcturus
taken about six months apart.*

(a) 1939 July 1
(b) 1940 January 19

according to their different wavelengths, a "spectrum"
is a record of this color separation. The chemical elements in a star cause some of the colors to be missing:
from a study of which colors are missing, scientists can
tell which elements are present.

It has been found, just as expected, that there are
some stars that contain almost no complicated elements. These are the oldest inhabitants of the Milky
Way, the stars that were formed when the original gas

cloud was nearly pure hydrogen, not yet enriched by the elements thrown off from old stars. Younger stars, which our spectrographs show have much larger quantities of the complicated elements, have been found, too. Our sun is one of these young stars, which is quite a good thing, because otherwise we wouldn't be here.

After a great deal of observation with telescopes, and careful study, we now know that our sun is about five billion years old, about one-quarter the age of the galaxy.

All this indicates what a busy place the Milky Way is. Stars are born, change their size, sometimes explode, and finally end as faint, tiny dwarfs. New stars are born, generation after generation, from the clouds that spin through space. Sometimes planets are formed, and sometimes living things, as we shall see. Man has hardly begun to know all the things that are in the Milky Way.

CHAPTER TWO

The Making of a Star

ALL the Milky Way is strewn with clouds of dust and gas rich with the elements that are needed to make planets and organic matter. Man has actually used his telescopes to see very young stars in space. Some in the sword of Orion, for instance, are probably not much more than 10 thousand years old, younger than the human race. From this and similar evidence it can be reasoned scientifically that new stars must be forming this very minute somewhere in the depths of space. If these can be seen and studied, we will be able to understand how a star is formed and, by using this knowledge, how planetary systems originate. From this information it will be possible to discover how many planetary systems there are and with which stars they are most likely to be found.

Our telescopes can be used to search among the dust clouds in an attempt to find the collections of dust that are beginning to become stars. The photograph of another galaxy in Andromeda, the spiral nebula, clearly shows the disk of dust and gas in this galaxy, similar to the disk in which our sun lies in the Milky Way. It is probably in such disks that most new star formations take place.

Very thick, small clouds of dust and gas have been located that seem to have separated from the larger clouds; these are so thick that they may well be taking the first steps toward becoming stars. We do not know all the various ways in which the dust clouds may be broken off from the large, thin clouds of the galaxy, but one activity that is busily producing them has been discovered. This is the activity created in the vicinity of a hot, new star after its birth.

When such a star is born, it floods the space around it with ultraviolet light. Some of this light comes from the sun, although our eyes are unable to see it; but it is the type of light that gives a sunburn, so we can be sure it is there. A star hotter than the sun pours much more intense ultraviolet light into space. This light is very easily captured by the gas clouds of space, which

Spiral galaxy in Andromeda.

turn the light into heat. In this way the gas clouds near a young star become very hot after the star starts shining. In fact, they become so hot that they glow, and it is easy to take pictures of this glow with our optical telescopes, as shown in earlier photographs in this book. Groups of hot, young stars are shown in the photographs of the bright nebula in the constellation Serpens, the Serpent, and the Rosette Nebula in the constellation Monoceros, the Unicorn.

When a gas is heated, its pressure increases, and it wants to push outward. It is this same principle that

The bright nebula in the constellation Serpens.

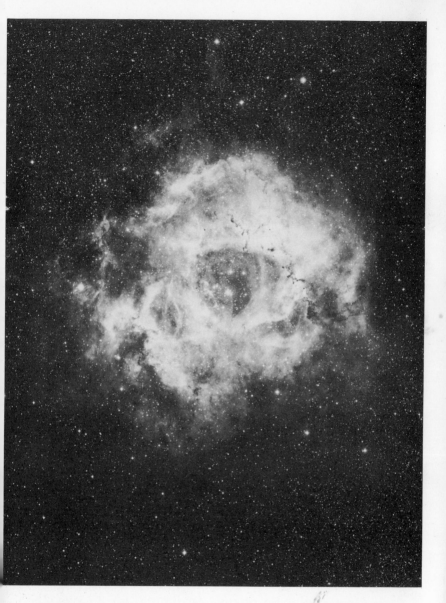

The Rosette Nebula.

is used to operate an automobile. There, some air and gasoline are sealed in a container (the engine cylinder). The gasoline is burned to heat the air, and this increases the pressure in the container, in turn pushing a piston out of the cylinder. The piston is connected by machinery to the wheels of the car and makes them turn. In space, the increased pressure in the gas also makes it push outward. It pushes against any clouds of dust and gas that may be near and, in fact, pushes so hard that it breaks pieces off the clouds and squeezes the pieces into thick globules. Note the many compact dark dust globules in the enlargement of the Rosette Nebula. This could well be the first step in the formation of a star. Perhaps there are other ways of breaking off such dust clouds.

Once a globule of dust has been created, the pressure of starlight and the gravitational pull of different parts of the globule on one another will cause it to get smaller and smaller. Eventually the globule may become little enough to be a star. Everything exerts a gravitational pull on everything else. The earth pulls on us; we pull on the earth. The reader and this book also have a gravitational pull on each other, but it is so small that one can't feel it. In space, however, the different parts of a dense ball of dust can pull on one another, and force themselves closer and closer together, although it may take many millions of years.

As the globule of dust is diminishing in size, the

An enlargement of a portion of the Rosette Nebula.

central parts of it are being compressed by the outer parts of the ball pushing inward. This makes the central parts increase in temperature, just as with the bicycle pump described earlier. Finally, they get so hot that nuclear reactions start, provide a great deal of heat, and the globule begins to shine as a star.

This theory seems to explain how stars originate, but still does not indicate the ways in which planets are formed. Some additional information will have to be considered in order to understand how the earth could have evolved.

Our whole Milky Way turns as a huge pinwheel about its center. Because it is turning, and also because the clouds collide with one another, every globule of gas is turning, too. Now, if something that is turning becomes increasingly smaller, it will turn more and more rapidly. This is how an ice skater manages to spin so quickly. He starts out spinning with his arms held out; then he pulls his arms in, making himself more compact. This makes him spin much faster, sometimes too fast: he falls down. This is happening to the globules of dust in space, too. They start out very large in size, and may actually begin with diameters 10 million times greater than that of a star. As the globules collapse to the size of a star, they too should spin with increasing speed, until they are spinning 10 million times faster than when they started. This is described by one of the best-known laws of physics, the Law of Conservation of Angular Momentum. However, if the sun, or any star, actually spun that rapidly, it would explode immediately. If the theory described earlier of the formation of a star were right, the globule of gas would rotate faster and faster as it got smaller and smaller, until, long before it was small enough to be a star, it would spin so fast that it would fly apart.

The same physical law that describes these difficulties also indicates a way to overcome them: it allows the transfer of spin from one body to another. In a way, this is what the rapidly spinning ice skater does when he puts out his arms to slow down; he is transferring some of his body's spin to his outstretched arms; as a result, his body slows down. This offers a solution to the problem of how a cloud collapses into a star without spinning so fast that it expodes. The cloud must transfer its spin to something else as it gets smaller. So, if we are to have a star at all, the cloud from which the star is forming must pass its spin to a separate piece of cloud, or perhaps several pieces which may continue to revolve around the star, perhaps in orbit. These separate pieces can then, themselves, contract into another star or perhaps planets. By taking a few measurements of the universe, and using the Law of Conservation of Angular Momentum, we have discovered that a star cannot be formed unless a second large object or group of objects is formed at the same time.

[43]

It is possible to look into space and find evidence that this theory is probably correct. Ninety-eight per cent of the spin in our own solar system is in the planets, showing that the sun was very efficient in transferring its spin to something else when it was formed. Moreover, when we carefully study the stars, it is found that approximately half of them are accompanied by another star, which orbits around the main star. Apparently, about half the time, when a star is born, the spin is passed to one separate large body that becomes a companion star. We find that the average distance between the members of a pair of stars is approximately the same as the distance from the sun to the major planets of our solar system: Jupiter, Saturn, Uranus, and Neptune. Most of the material of the planetary system lies in those planets. It may have been only good luck that a planetary system was formed when the sun was formed, rather than a second star.

Half the stars in the sky are not accompanied by other stars—at least it has not been possible to detect such second stars. They must, however, be accompanied by something, or they could not have been formed. Our solar system suggests what that might be: a family of planets. Unfortunately, we cannot yet build a telescope powerful enough to find planets of other solar systems, not even those that may accompany the nearest stars. Therefore, we must trust the conclusions our minds reach from the observable facts. It seems reasonable to conclude that almost every star in the sky that seems alone actually possesses a family of planets. There will soon be telescopes that may be able to prove this by actually detecting evidence of other planetary systems.

In order to explain the formation of a star, it is necessary to assume the transfer of spin to a second body of dust. From what astronomers have seen in the sky, we may conclude that this second body of dust in turn becomes either a star or a group of planets. This second body of dust has become a family of planets in the case of one star: the sun. Moreover, everything known about the sun says it is the most average of stars.

Would it not then seem reasonable to suppose that the sun's planet companions are average, too; that the universe is the home of many worlds much like ours; and that even the living things of the earth are average? This would mean that countless times during the history of our galaxy, life, even intelligent life, has arisen.

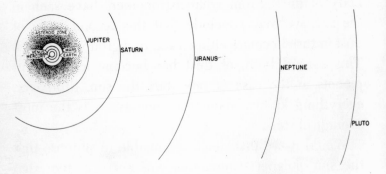

Relative distances of the planets revolving around our sun.

CHAPTER THREE

Where Can Life Originate?

INNUMERABLE planets are almost certainly revolving around their suns throughout the Milky Way. On them may be life; but we still do not really *know* if living things will arise and advance on any of these planets. To know this, it is necessary to learn more about the way organisms originate and develop.

A few pages ago it was stated that living matter is made of complicated combinations of certain elements, with the element carbon among the most important. Carbon is very remarkable in that its atoms are capable of joining together with themselves and with atoms of other elements. In this way large interconnected combinations of atoms are formed. Few other elements can do this, and none is able to do it so well. An enormous number of combinations of carbon atoms with other atoms can be made by chemists. The materials produced in this way are commonly called organic compounds, the word "organic" being related to the organs of living things, which are always composed of these substances. Organic compounds are the basis of both living things and a host of other materials: oil, gasoline, medicines, and even plastic dishpans.

The important point to be considered in the search for other intelligent life is that all living things on earth are made of organic substances. These substances have been studied very carefully in the chemical laboratory to see how they are made and what happens to them at different temperatures, pressures, and so on. One area of particular study has been the changes, called reactions, that are connected with the processes of life. These are the reactions that make living things grow, eat, breathe, reproduce, and perform other functions. It has been learned that the reactions necessary to produce life happen only within a certain range of temperatures. These temperatures must usually be between the freezing and boiling point of water, that is, between 32° and 212° Fahrenheit. If the temperature were lower than 32°, the reactions would take place so slowly that they would not produce organic matter, or the living thing would freeze. If the temperature were higher than 212°, the reactions would usually not occur as they normally do. Rather, the organism would be destroyed instead of engaging in the life processes.

These facts indicate the planets on which we will *not* find life. A planet too close to its star would be subject to such bright "starlight" that the temperature everywhere would be above the boiling point of water. The planet could not have life. Mercury and Venus in our own solar system are in this state. Every planet that is so far away from its star that its temperature is always below freezing will probably not have life. All the planets beyond Mars in our system—Jupiter, Saturn, Uranus, Neptune, and Pluto—seem to be in this condition. Most of the planets in space, therefore, are either too hot or too cold to support life. That should leave, however, an enormous number of hospitable planets. The dark markings, visible on the surface in all the photographs of Mars but *D*, change in intensity with the Martian seasons. It has been found by spectrographic studies that material in the dark regions probably contains' hydrogen and carbon atoms joined together, which appears to be evidence for life on Mars. The white area in *D* is one of the polar caps of Mars.

An artist's conception of the part of Mercury on the borderland between the dark and sunlit sides of the planet.

Imaginative conception of the landscape of the sunlit side of Mercury.

*An artist's conception of the dark side of Mercury,
always turned away from the sun.*

Venus.

Saturn.

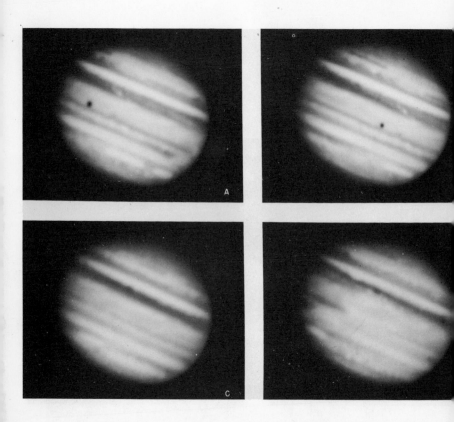

Jupiter. In A the shadow of a satellite is visible.
In B, both the satellite and its shadow are visible.

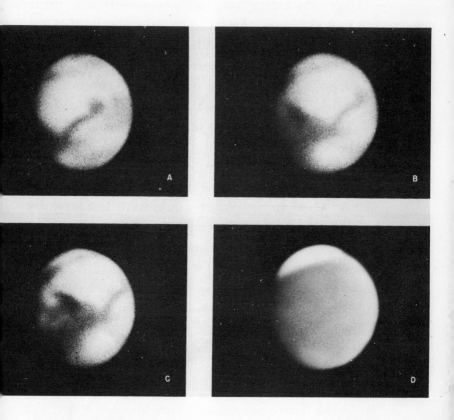

Mars.

These strict temperature requirements also make life impossible on planets traveling in orbits that are elliptical, or egg-shaped, rather than circular. Although the planets of the solar system, with the exception of Pluto, go in nearly circular orbits, planets do not *have* to do this. There are probably planets that follow very elliptical orbits, just as some of our artificial earth satellites do. Such an orbit means that the planet will occasionally be very close to its star and then swing far away from it. If these changes in distance were to vary enough, the planet would have temperatures too hot or cold for life, and living things would not be able to survive. This fact may eliminate many planets as possible homes for living things. Any planets that exist in double-star systems are almost certainly ruled out, because the presence of two stars makes a planet follow a very erratic and wandering path that will almost certainly produce temperatures unsuitable for life.

Stars that are variable in brightness can also be excluded. There are actually very many of these. For example, the so-called Cepheid variables, named after the constellation Cepheus (the father of Andromeda) in the northern sky where the first member of the group was identified, roughly double their brightness in a few days or weeks at regular intervals. The North Star is one of these, although its changes in brightness are much smaller than average.

More spectacular are the giant red variable stars that may change their brightness by as much as a hundred times in a few months; these were described in Chapter One. The most famous of the giant red variables is the star Mira, the Wonderful, in the constellation of Cetus, the Whale. Such changes in brightness would of course change the temperatures on any planets so much as to prevent or destroy life. ✓

Earlier, the way in which a star becomes larger and brighter, after it has used up most of the hydrogen in its central parts, was described. Obviously, this increase in brightness, with its resultant increase in temperature, would destroy any life that has arisen on a planet. So, if advanced forms of life, including intelligent beings, are ever to develop on a planet, the star's increase in brightness must be delayed for as long as it takes to develop an intelligent species.

Approximately how long a star can remain at the same level of brightness before it begins to get larger and brighter is now known. This length of time is short for very massive stars, and longer for those that are less massive. It is known that the sun can last about 10 billion years before it will start getting much brighter. About five billion years were necessary to develop intelligent creatures on the earth. This means, if the earth is typical, that any star that starts becoming a giant star in less than about five billion years will probably never support intelligent life. It will destroy life on its planets before there is time for an intelligent creature to develop. Our computations show that stars more massive than the sun will stay at constant brightness too short a time. Thus, the unhappy decision is reached that all of these stars can never support intelligent beings.

Stars a good deal less massive than the sun are not likely to have life either. There is only a small range of distances near these much more faint stars in which planets will have the right temperatures. When this range becomes very small, it is unlikely that a planet will be found in it. Even in our own solar system, only two planets, Mars and the earth, fall within the life-bearing zone surrounding the sun.

When the reasons why different kinds of stars cannot have planets with intelligent life are considered, it is necessary to eliminate many, many stars as likely homes for civilizations. In fact, only those that are similar to our sun are left as candidates. However, when stars with uninviting conditions for life have been eliminated, there remains about one star in ten that probably has planets on which intelligent life could live. In the whole Milky Way, there are many more than a billion stars with the right conditions to sustain intelligent beings.

CHAPTER FOUR

The Creatures of the Earth

MORE than a billion places for creatures to live in space! How often will life exist? Even when a planet orbits around a sun under conditions that give the proper temperature range to sustain life, organisms do not necessarily appear. Perhaps, however, the development of life is not as difficult as has always been thought.

Some years ago at the University of Chicago, Stanley Miller, a young scientist about to complete his studies, conducted an experiment reproducing what probably happened in the air of the earth shortly after our planet was formed.

The original composition of the earth's atmosphere was much different from that of today. Instead of containing primarily the elements nitrogen and oxygen, as it does now, the air contained a group of much different substances. These were probably ammonia (which, dissolved in water, is used for household cleaning), hydrogen gas, water, and methane (the inflammable gas that can be smelled near some swamps). The atmospheres of the larger planets are still made up of these same gases.

Miller tightly sealed a mixture of these gases in a jar, using proportions that are believed to be about the same as the early atmosphere of the earth. He then passed electrical-spark discharges through it; these discharges simulated lightning. After a few days, he studied the contents of the jar to see if there was any change, and if so, what new substances had been formed. In the drawing depicting some of the transformations Miller observed, H represents a hydrogen atom, O oxygen, C carbon, and N nitrogen. To his amazement, he found that large organic molecules, containing many atoms, had been built up from the very simple ones that originally had been in the jar. Among these organic molecules were the amino acids "glycine" and "alanine." This was an important discovery, because amino acids are the basic building blocks from which the very large and complex organic protein molecules are constructed; it is from proteins

H │ -O	O=C=O	H │ H–C–H │ H	H–H	H │ N–H │ H
ter	Carbon dioxide	Methane	Hydrogen	Ammonia

+   Lightning
     Ionizing Radiation   Give
     Ultra-violet Light

O ‖ C–OH	H O │ ‖ H–C–C–OH │ H	O H H O ‖ │ │ ‖ HO–C–C–C–C–OH │ │ H H	H O │ ‖ H–C–C–OH │ H–N │ H
rmic cid	Acetic acid	Succinic· acid	Glycine

Some of the chemical transformations that took place in Stanley Miller's experiments.

that living things are made. Miller found that lightning probably was instrumental in manufacturing the amino acids that were created in the early days of the earth's history. Nuclear radiation, which comes continuously to the earth from space, could have effected the same reaction. No extraordinary or rare event is needed to produce the basic materials of life.

A living thing is composed basically of two particular types of organic chemical. One type consists of protein molecules, which act in the organism like

[61]

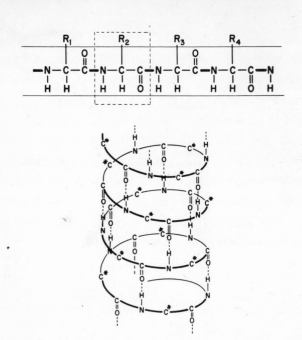

A typical protein molecule.

factory workers, helping to convert food into new living material. Nucleic acids are the other type; they are the "blueprints" of an organism, telling the proteins what to produce. The figures are a representation of the complex structure of these very large molecules, showing the way atoms are believed to combine. In the drawing of the protein molecule, R_1, R_2, and R_3 are symbols for three different groups of atoms that occur in protein molecules; in that of nucleic acid, P represents an atom of the element phosphorus.

[62]

We have seen how the materials necessary to make proteins would have been generated in the atmosphere of the early earth by lightning or some other powerful process. The nucleic acids could have been made in the same way, although this is not definitely known. However, scientists have recently discovered a way in which fragments of nucleic acids *have* been arriving on the earth: they are carried in meteorites. Meteorites are stony or metallic objects from outer space that collide with the earth.

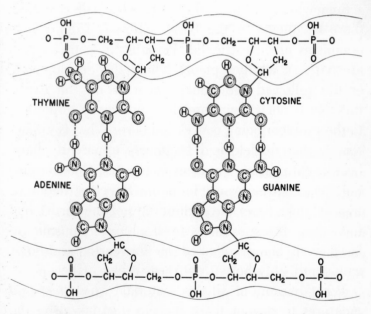

A nucleic-acid molecule.

Recently, a careful study was made of the materials inside a meteorite that fell in Calloway County, Ky., in 1950. The results of this study indicate the presence of many organic chemicals in the meteorite. In particular, the study shows good evidence for the presence of nucleic acid fragments. However, no fragments of proteins were found in this meteorite. Scientists have recently found that other meteorites contain in their interiors large organic molecules; in fact, some of these molecules might once have been part of a living thing.

Somewhere in space the meteorites had collected these fragments of the basic materials from which organisms are constructed. Perhaps these meteorites are parts of another planet where the development of life followed the same course as on the earth. But this is not known, and it is not really important to the problem being considered here. What *is* important is that nucleic-acid fragments apparently have been arriving from space on meteorites, thus supplying the second necessary factor for the construction of living things. From the earliest days of the earth's history, then, the substances from which organisms are built were being collected on the earth, and so it would probably be with any earth-like planet.

What became of all this material? There were no creatures to devour it, so it simply gathered on the earth, most of it probably being dissolved in the oceans. Billions of years went by, while the oceans became richer and richer in organic molecules. It is probable, though not yet certain, that over this long period of time some of these molecules joined together to make larger units, and these connected with others to become still larger.

Finally, about two and a half billion years ago, a group of molecules may have come together in a unique combination that could take other, simpler molecules from the ocean and make a duplicate of itself. This was the first living thing. It was the most primitive of creatures, but one that could take "food" from the vast supply that was in the ocean, and reproduce its kind. Life had developed on the earth.

These last steps have never been duplicated in the laboratory, but scientists are trying hard to do this right now. They are tracing, one after another, the processes by which life may have developed from nonliving material. Someday we may know exactly the way in which this very important development occurred.

The descendants of this first organism probably multiplied rapidly. They had an ocean full of food, and there was no struggle with other forms of life for their nourishment. Then, for the first time in the history of life on the earth, a crisis developed: almost all the food was eaten. The ocean, which had been a rich source of food when the organisms first developed, was almost completely barren. At this point, an event most important to the development of intelligent life occurred: the competition to survive began.

As soon as the food supply became limited, organisms competed with one another for nourishment. Those who were in some way stronger survived; the rest did not. Tragedy appeared on the earth.

If all these organisms had been developed from the same nucleic acid, they would have been identical. None would be stronger than the other. This was not so, because during all the years the organisms were multiplying, the composition of the nucleic acids was changing. Every second, very powerful nuclear particles, cosmic rays, had come crashing into the earth's atmosphere from the depths of space. This bombardment still goes on today. These particles are probably created in the supernova explosions mentioned earlier. They are shot from the supernovae into space, through which they travel in great curved paths for many years before entering the earth's atmosphere. When cosmic rays strike the atoms of the air, they dislodge more nuclear particles. Eventually many particles strike the surface of the earth as a result of one that comes crashing in from far out in space.

As this book is being read, these particles are flying through the room. They cannot be seen or felt. Nevertheless, when the particles strike a living thing, they sometimes cause a rearrangement of a few atoms in it.

This rearrangement went on continuously in the first organisms on the earth. Sometimes an atom in the nucleic acid was changed; then the "blueprint" did not give the same instructions as before, and the new organisms made from it were slightly different from the original. Such variations are called mutations. Usually mutations are not as efficient and strong as the original, but sometimes a mutation is in some way an improvement. In such a way, the organisms that filled the ocean in those early days began to vary, and some were better than others. In the competition that took place, the strongest survived.

Ever since there has been a shortage of food on the earth, there has been constant competition for survival. This struggle and the continual production of new mutations have caused the creatures of the earth to improve continuously, a process called evolution.

At some time during the long pageant of evolution, green plants containing chlorophyll appeared, and the process called photosynthesis, by which plants make food, went into action. In photosynthesis, plants take in water and carbon dioxide and, using the energy from sunlight, convert these materials into large organic molecules called carbohydrates, which are food for the plant. During photosynthesis free oxygen gas is formed, which is released into the atmosphere. Oxygen in the atmosphere of a planet, then, is a clue to the presence of life there, too. In this way the makeup of the atmosphere was changed as plants flooded it with oxygen.

In time, all the free hydrogen that had been present in the primitive atmosphere was lost to space. Hydrogen is a very light element, and when its atoms or molecules (each molecule contains two atoms of hydrogen joined together) are heated to the normal temperature of the upper part of our atmosphere, some of them are moving so rapidly that they fly off into space, never to return. As this process continued, more and more hydrogen was lost until, finally, all the hydrogen disappeared. At the same time, nitrogen was being released into the atmosphere from the outer layers of the earth. Before too long, the original atmosphere was gone, and in its place was an atmosphere like the one on the earth today, consisting mainly of oxygen and nitrogen.

Lightning bolts can no longer produce the bases of living things on the earth, because the right elements are not uniquely present. The earth can probably never again give rise to life from its first stages.

Let us go on with the drama of evolution of life on the earth. In some places, layers of mud, now turned to stone, have been laid one on top of another, year after year, forming sedimentary rocks. As one digs down through these rocks, he is going back in time. Sometimes fossils, impressions or remains of things that lived when that particular layer was at the earth's

A fossil fish.

surface, can be found. In this way the scientist can trace the history of living things.

The study of fossils has shown that organisms have continuously grown more complex. Life on the earth has progressed from very simple, primitive organisms to rudimentary plants and shellfish; then, through more complicated plants and fish to amphibians, animals, and plants that can live in both air and water. Next to develop were the giant reptiles, the greatest of which were the dinosaurs.

Approximately 70 million years ago, an unknown catastrophe greatly affected life on the earth. It may have been the coming of a great ice age, when most of the earth was covered by ice and snow, or perhaps something as exotic as a supernova explosion very close to the earth. The end result of this mysterious event was the almost total annihilation of the reptiles ruling the earth, and the sudden dominance of animal life like that on the earth today. The greatest advance in evolution appeared approximately 100 thousand years ago; this is just a small fraction of a cosmic year ago. This greatest advance was the appearance of human beings like ourselves.

What made man so skillful in the competition for food? He was much smaller and weaker than many of the species he was struggling against. In fact, the one characteristic that has made him the high point in evolution is *intelligence:* the ability to think, talk, and remember. Also, man is capable of recording his knowledge for others to use; the store of human knowledge and the ability to solve problems of survival continually grow. For example, one may not have the least idea where and how to drill an oil well, but if the information is needed, it can be found in books on the subject. One of the most fundamental features of evolution is the continuous improvement in intelligence made by the creatures of the earth.

The Creatures of the Earth

All successful creatures must have a very great desire to survive. This means they must usually be skillful fighters when they are attacked or think they must defend themselves. Sometimes these creatures are so quick to fight that they are called aggressive. Intelligent as man has become, he still retains some of the aggressiveness that has been important in his struggle for survival through the centuries. Mankind has had many wars, and men still fight among themselves. Today, this is very dangerous because man's intelligence has given him the means by which he could destroy himself and all other life on earth. If, through some folly, this great disaster should happen, life may not appear again. Surprisingly, this must be taken into account when calculating the possibilities of finding intelligent life in space.

It has been seen that the formation of the substances from which living things are made is extremely probable on a planet like ours. Just as probable, to the best of our knowledge, is the eventual development of an intelligent species when the food supply becomes insufficient and competition for it begins. These developments would be likely to happen on any life-bearing planet, although perhaps more slowly on some than on others. If the earth is typical, every one of the planets capable of supplying the necessary conditions for life that were discussed in the last chapter may have intelligent beings living on it, if it is five billion or more years old.

Our own planetary system will prove whether this theory is correct. Within its life-bearing zone, there are but two planets, the earth and Mars. The earth has developed its intelligent species. Space probes to other planets will, in the near future, greatly clarify the theories of the possibility of life in space. Already, on Mars can be seen dark regions that change with the seasons and quickly reappear even when covered with a thick blanket of dust. Evidence of large organic molecules has been found with spectrographs. In fact, it is almost certain that there is life on Mars, but a very primitive, little-evolved life. Mars has not yet produced its intelligent species. However, every planet that man can examine, and that has the right temperature for life, does seem to bear life. The conclusions that have been reached about the possibilities of other intelligent life appear to be correct. All across the galaxy, then, time after time, intelligent beings and civilizations have probably arisen and may be arising today.

What would be more fascinating than to talk to a person from another planet, to hear of his history, of what he enjoys, and of what he believes to be beautiful? If this could happen, it would be perhaps the most exciting adventure in the history of mankind.

CHAPTER FIVE

The Most Difficult Problem

THE next chapter will be devoted to the problem of finding the cheapest and best way to contact other civilizations. The last chapter showed that, very probably, many intelligent species have developed in space; although exactly how many is not known, there have probably been more than one can imagine. Nevertheless, before this engineering problem can be approached, it is necessary to have an idea as to the distance to the nearest civilization using methods of communication.

Why a "communicating" civilization? This is quite different from any other kind of civilization, and the difference is important. Listening for a radio message from another civilized world would be useless if that world did not use radio. Every civilization will probably develop science and technology at some time in its history, just as we have. However, some will be behind us; and others that have progressed beyond us may no longer be using communication techniques. The distance to the nearest civilization with which we may converse may be very short, only a few light-years. A light-year is the distance light travels in one year, about six trillion miles. The nearest star, not counting the sun, is about four light-years away.

Other civilizations might not be as eager to find intelligent life as we are. Many enthusiasms become less exciting with repetition, and eventually seem dull and tedious. Most of mankind's interests are constantly changing. A hundred years ago it was a great adventure to explore the South Seas; today space is the challenge. So it may be with space research, and perhaps even science; the great wonder of today may be the dull history of a few hundred years from now. Intelligent beings of other planets may well have evolved in the way man has, and be as changeable.

Still other factors could bring an end to man's desire to reach communicative civilizations: a cosmic accident, for instance, such as the collision of an asteroid with the earth. The examination of space, however, shows that any serious cosmic accident is not likely.

Finally, there is the possibility mentioned at the end of the previous chapter: man's nuclear skill could lead to the termination of his communicative state.

Now, the number of communicating civilizations in the Milky Way is proportional to their average communicating lifetimes. If at a given time the Milky Way has a million communicative civilizations, average lifetimes twice as long for these civilizations would mean there would be two million of them. This is because, as we have seen, civilizations are always arising. If there is one new civilization each year, which is probably close to the right figure, and the average communicative lifetime is 100 years, there will be only 100 communicative civilizations in the Milky Way at any time. Consider an instant when there are no civilizations using methods of communication. Then after one year there will be one, after two years, two, and so on, until after 100 years there will be 100. In the hundred and first year a new one would appear, but the civilization that arose during the first year would die. The total remains 100, and so it will remain indefinitely. The number of communicative civilizations will be the product of the rate at which these civilizations occur (one per year in the above example), times the average communicative lifetime (100 years in the above example). The number will thus stay constant, although the civilizations making up the group would be continuously changing.

The preceding chapters gave information about the rate at which communicative civilizations appear. The other necessary figure, which is equally important, is the average time during which a civilization will use methods of communication. There is the *real* problem. Somewhere, locked up inside mankind, is the answer, but it is still too early in the lifetime of our own civilization to know how wise man is going to be in using the great marvels of modern science or how long he will remain interested in them. The answers have to be guessed, and these guesses are probably much less accurate than the approximation of how many planets there are, or how often civilizations arise.

Let us assume that nuclear war never eliminates life from the planet, that men continue to search the depths of space for several thousand years. If the earth and other civilizations do have this long as communicative civilizations, knowledge of the Milky Way would indicate that the average distance between these civilizations is something like one thousand light-years.

Man then has a good chance to find other civilizations if he has instruments that are capable of reaching across a thousand light-years and finding signs of any efforts of another civilization to communicate. These instruments do exist.

CHAPTER SIX

Reaching to the Stars

M A N wishes to detect the presence of intelligent life on planets of distant stars. As is often the case, there is more than one way to do this, but most desirable is the method that is most efficient and economical; this will also be the most likely method by which other planets might be trying to reach the earth.

One of the first possibilities that occurs to people is that other communicative civilizations will be using highly complicated, expensive means to talk to us. This seems likely because these civilizations should be more advanced than man is, and so have much greater engineering skill. It is true that in most cases the other civilization will be more advanced. If the civilizations in space could be observed, it would be found that they were evenly spread in development over the whole communicative period. Many would have existed thousands of years longer than man's short civilized history. Any civilization found is therefore likely to be ahead of the earth in development.

Even though they are more advanced, these civilizations will still use the easiest and least expensive means of accomplishing the goals they set themselves, such as discovering other intelligent life. There are many things that men know how to do in different ways, but they always use the cheapest way. For instance, an office building a mile high could be built, but is not, because it is cheaper to construct several smaller buildings with a total of the same office space. Or, to take a more obvious example, there are several ways to eradicate mosquitoes. DDT is one method, but it could also be done by loading all the soldiers of the United States Army in helicopters with machineguns and flying them over swamps, guns blazing away. This is not a very efficient way to kill mosquitoes. So it will be in space: even with more advanced civilizations, the most economical methods will be used for interstellar communications. Now, what possible ways are there to be considered?

Everyone is familiar with the method shown quite often on cereal boxes: spaceships can be sent to the moon, and past Venus; these rockets will be large enough to carry Collier's Encyclopedia, for example. A great deal of information could be sent in this way.

The stars, however, are much farther away than Venus or the moon. Venus is only a few light-minutes away, while stars with planetary systems having intelligent life may be a thousand light-years away. Physicists now believe that nothing can go faster than the speed of light, and light takes a thousand years to go a thousand light-years. It will take at least four years to communicate with the nearest star, and four more for an answer to get back, if the message travels at the speed of light.

An enormous amount of energy must be used to push a rocket to nearly the speed of light. In fact, it has been computed that sending Collier's Encyclopedia across space at 99 per cent of the speed of light would require a rocket that weighed, at takeoff, a *billion* times more than the encyclopedia. It is only possible to use this minimal amount of energy and weight if the most efficient energy-producing process that has been conceived is used: a technique that would convert hydrogen into helium. A rocket using this process does not exist, and will not for a very long time. Even if such an energy supply were available, a rocket weighing roughly 100 billion pounds would be needed to send Collier's Encyclopedia into space. One hundred billion pounds is the weight of a thousand battleships. Just to launch the rocket, we would have to expand the Cape Canaveral base until it was approximately the size of the whole state of Florida.

Sending any *object* to other stars so rapidly is fairly preposterous then. It is also unlikely that spaceships from other stars will visit the earth. Probes can be sent to our sister planets, all right, because they can travel relatively slowly on these trips, but they could not go to the stars. As the Nobel Prize-winning American physicist, E. M. Purcell, has said, such dreams belong right back where they came from, on the cereal box.

If interstellar communication is to exist it will very probably be by a more efficient and cheaper method.

The astronomer R. N. Bracewell, of Stanford University, has suggested that advanced civilizations wanting to contact other beings will send out automatic space probes traveling at much less than the speed of light to visit other stars, search for life, and radio back a message if some sign of life is found. As long as there was no hurry to find out if life existed in space, this system might be possible, but it is not very economical, either. Earlier, it was estimated that the average distance between communicative civilizations might be one thousand light-years. If so, less than one in a million stars will possess a planet with intelligent life using methods of communication. More than a million space probes would have to be sent into space in order to have a good chance of finding just one civilization. This is about equivalent to the one-thousand-battleship problem again. Besides, there would be no humans along to repair the space probes if they broke down or were destroyed by meteors: replacement probes would then have to be sent out continuously.

Man really wants to send *information*, not objects, which have been shown to be too difficult and expensive to transport. The transmission of instructions as to how to make the objects is a better method; then the beings with whom we are conversing can have the information without the objects actually crossing space.

There is an inexpensive and effective way to send *information* across space very quickly, and we use it all the time: *radio*. Radio waves and television waves, which are the same thing, travel across space at the speed of light, as fast as anything can go. All they can carry is information, and they do that very well and cheaply. Radio waves are generated from electrical power, which is inexpensive; a penny's worth of electrical energy will keep an average light bulb lit for about a day. Radio waves are also cheap because a machine that will convert large amounts of electrical power into radio power does not cost much to build. Receivers that can detect very faint radio signals are also inexpensive to make.

If the largest radio transmitters and antennas on the earth were used to send 60 words of information, say a telegram, one light-year into space, the price of the electrical energy needed to perform this job would be one nickel. This means that for approximately half a million dollars' worth of electrical energy, we could send Collier's Encyclopedia to the nearest stars. That is less than it costs to send a single large rocket into space, and much less than the cost of a thousand battleships. In fact, it is an amount our country can easily afford today.

In order to construct the proper equipment and method for sending these messages it is necessary to know something about radio. Radio waves are known to physicists as electromagnetic waves. They are energy-carrying packets of vibrations that are both electrical and magnetic at the same time, hence the name. These waves travel through completely empty space at the speed of light; light, too, is an electro-magnetic wave. The only difference between light and radio waves is the frequency of their vibrations. The frequency, or number of times per second wave peaks or troughs pass an observer, is much higher in light waves.

As the waves travel through space, they become weaker as a result of a scientific law known as the inverse square law. This law states that electromagnetic radiation becomes weaker in proportion to the square of the distance through which it has traveled. A wave that has a certain intensity after traveling one light-year will be one-quarter as strong after traveling two light-years, and one-ninth as strong after three light-years. We have all seen this happen as we got nearer to or farther from light sources. Because of this law, much more power is needed as messages are sent over longer distances.

Radio transmitters convert and modulate the source of electrical power into power vibrating at radio frequencies. They then transmit this power to the antenna. If a proper antenna is used, this radio frequency power will be sent off into space as radio waves.

Antennas are constructed in many different ways. The simplest antennas radiate, or send off into space, radio waves in almost all directions at once. Since as much power as possible should be directed at a particular star, this type of antenna would be rather wasteful. Antennas that do send power primarily in one direction have been built. The large 300-foot radio telescope of the National Radio Astronomy Observatory in Fig. 28 is an example of one of these. Some of the antennas that are being constructed are capable of concentrating radio waves in one direction so well that the waves are 10 million times stronger in that direction than if they were being radiated in all directions. In such a case, we say the gain is 10 million.

Large gain is very helpful, because it means a much smaller transmitter may be used than when the power is sent in all directions. Another way to say this is that a message can be sent about three thousand times farther with this strongly directional antenna than without it, remembering the inverse square law.

After the radio waves are sent into space, they continue to lose their intensity following the inverse square law until they strike a receiving antenna. Receiving antennas, which are designed and built in the same way as transmitting antennas, collect some of the radio waves that strike them and convert them back into electrical power, again vibrating at the radio frequency. They then feed this power to the radio receiver.

The radio receiver is an apparatus that can detect and measure very small amounts of electrical power vibrating at radio frequencies. It is constructed to select only a very narrow range, or "band," of frequencies to which it responds. This is necessary for two reasons. First, there are usually many radio signals being sent at once, and the receiver must eliminate all but the one it should receive. Second, there is static, or "noise," generated in the receiver itself and also picked up by the antenna from space that tends to overwhelm and hide the signal being received. This is the same as the static in a radio, or the "snow" on a TV screen. The noise is generated on all frequencies, so if

*The National Radio Astronomy
Observatory's 300-foot telescope.*

the receiver were to receive them all, there would be a great deal of interference and it would be very difficult to locate the signal. Recently a special kind of radio telescope with a "horn" antenna was constructed at Andover, Maine, for use with communications satellites. It has recently been used with the Telstar satellite and has been found to pick up much less noise from the earth. To reduce this received noise, it would be desirable to cut down the range of frequencies received, or the "bandwidth," until it is no larger than the band of frequencies over which the signal power has been sent. When this is done, as much unwanted noise as possible is eliminated, but all the signal power comes through. After a certain point, it is not possible to make the bandwidth smaller without throwing away signal power, which would again not be satisfactory.

If the transmitted signal of our cosmic radio link were sent at constant frequency, it would be at one frequency at all times, and would occupy no bandwidth at all. The receiver bandwidth could then be extremely small and eliminate a great deal of unwanted noise. This could not practically be done because we want to *say* something with our signal. This means its strength has to be changed at intervals following some code, or its frequency changed to convey the message, as in FM radio. Either action actually causes the signal to arrive on several different fre-

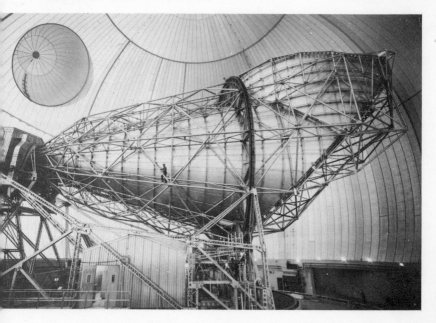

The horn antenna constructed at Andover, Maine.

quencies, and a bandwidth that covers at least a small range must be used.

An appreciable band of frequencies will have to be included in the receiver for another reason. Our transmitters and receivers will be in orbit about something: a star or a planet. Because of the orbital motion, the speed of the receiver and transmitter with respect to one another will be always changing. This will cause a change in the frequency of the waves coming to the receiving antenna, due to what is known as the Doppler effect. This is the same effect that causes the pitch of a train whistle to appear to change as the train goes by the hearer. When the train is approaching, the whistle sounds higher in pitch (frequency) than when the train is traveling away from the listener. The same thing will happen to the signals between stars. When the transmitter and receiver are coming toward each other the received frequency is higher than when they are moving apart. By utilizing an appreciable band of frequencies, it is possible to pick up the signal even though its frequency is constantly changing.

In recent years, some new kinds of radio receivers have been invented that are far more sensitive than the best old-style tube receivers. These new receivers are extraordinary devices making use of the special materials developed by the science known as solid-state physics. Solid-state physics is one of the fastest-advancing sciences; it deals with the properties of and ways to improve materials. As a result of the work done in this science, many new materials having very special properties have been invented.

Surprisingly, one of these materials is a modification of the ancient jewel, the ruby. When this newly invented variation, of the ruby is surrounded by a magnet, and cooled to very low temperatures, about 450° below zero, it becomes an amplifier of radio waves; that is, the ruby increases the strength of any radio power entering it. In order to act as an amplifier the ruby must be surrounded with some special electrical circuits, and power "pumped" into it at a frequency that is different from the one being amplified. This device is called a "maser," and it can be used to make the most sensitive receivers man now knows how to construct. These maser receivers are as much as 100 times more sensitive than the tube receivers. It is unfortunate that they cost so much more than tube receivers, because otherwise masers would be very useful in television-set construction.

Another modern wonder device is called a parametric amplifier. This is a very sensitive amplifier that uses a different kind of crystal developed by the solid-state physicists. It has advantages over a maser in that it does not need a magnet, or even low temperatures, for operation: it will operate quite well at room temperature. But the parametric amplifier is not usually as sensitive as a maser. The amplifier shown in Fig. 31 is a newly developed type that achieves a sensitivity nearly as high as the best maser when the amplifier is cooled to the temperature of liquid nitrogen, about −320F°. For very special projects, such as the search for other civilizations, where very high sensitivity is needed, a maser is the better instrument.

It is hard to appreciate fully the very great advance in sensitivity these remarkable technical developments

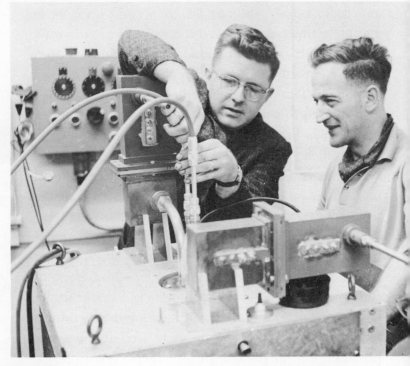

R. W. DeGrasse and H. E. D. Scovil, of the Bell Telephone Laboratories, making final adjustments on the maser used in the horn antenna shown in the previous illustration. This equipment has been used to relay television programs across the Atlantic Ocean for the first time.

K. M. Eisele making adjustments on the low-noise parametric amplifier developed by the Bell Telephone Laboratories.

have given us. When the antennas of a few years ago are compared with the very high-gain antennas now available, and with the advances in sensitivity given by the devices mentioned above, we find that our over-all ability to perceive, by radio, has improved almost 100 thousand times.

This is as great an advance as the invention of the telescope. In fact, it is a bigger improvement than has occurred in the whole development of optical tele-scopes from the first such instrument, which was about 3 inches in diameter and had only Galileo's eye to measure brightness, to the 200-inch telescope of today, with its sophisticated electronic detectors or photo-graphic plates. With the new equipment some great and thought-provoking discoveries may soon be made. Such previously impossible projects as detecting other intelligent beings suddenly have become possible; but without these brilliant advances in technology, they still would not be.

Listening with large radio telescopes is now not only practical, but the most inexpensive and best method of searching for other civilizations. Other new engineering marvels may make different methods fea-sible, too. After all, radio waves make up only a small portion of the electromagnetic waves that exist; that is, they are only a small portion of the electromagnetic spectrum. Other electromagnetic waves—ordinary light, gamma rays, X rays, infrared light—should be

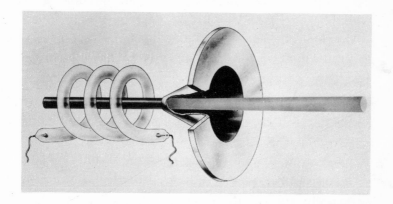

Pulsed ruby optical maser.

considered. Right now our technology knows most about the usefulness of radio frequencies, but future technological developments may make other frequencies, such as the light frequencies, as good or even better means for the search for intelligent life.

Just recently, a new device has appeared in the laboratories of the solid-state physicists that someday may make communication among the stars by light waves possible. This device, which operates much like the maser mentioned above, is called a laser, or optical maser, and sometimes uses variations of rubies, too. It

[93]

provides, for the first time, a transmitter for light waves that is really efficient as compared with the light bulb, which is a very poor transmitter.

One reason the laser is so efficient is that it concentrates light power in a narrow range of frequencies. Just as with radio, this narrowing permits the elimination of interference as much as possible and gives us the best sensitivity. The laser also emits its light in a very concentrated beam, which can be further focused to an even more compact beam through the use of an ordinary optical telescope; optical telescopes are very good antennas for light waves.

In fact, the gain of optical telescopes, using them as antennas, is much greater than the gain of even our best radio telescopes. An excellent 200-inch telescope, for instance, has a gain of as much as a million billion, very much greater than the best radio-telescope gains of 10 million. However, the advantages of this great gain are partially lost by the fact that the existing lasers are not nearly as powerful as the best radio transmitters. They are still a new invention, however; no one can guess how powerful they may be a few years from now. In the light-communication system shown, an ordinary telescope is used as a transmitter to focus into a narrow beam the radiation from a laser. This beam may spread out only a few feet in going hundreds of miles. Another telescope and a photocell are used to receive signals. The "compound Fabry-

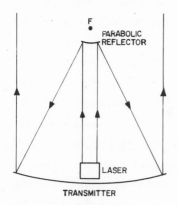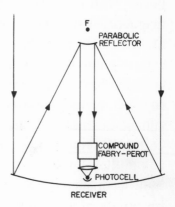

A light communication system.

Perot" shown in the drawing is a special filter that rejects all light except that at the frequency of the signal. A system much like this was recently used to send a light signal to the moon and back. The powerful and narrow beam of the transmitter struck an area of only a few miles on the moon's surface. The area reflected a tiny fraction of the power back to the telescope on the earth, the round trip taking about two and a half seconds.

[95]

Good receivers for light waves have been in use for a long time; these are sensitive photoelectric cells, sometimes called electric eyes. One of these, coupled to a large optical telescope, is a fine light-wave receiver. However, these photoelectric cells can never be as sensitive as the best radio receivers. Electromagnetic waves come in little units of energy, or quanta; these units of light or radio waves carry only certain amounts of energy. At radio frequencies they actually carry only about one-millionth the energy of the quanta at light frequencies. Less than one unit cannot be received, no matter how sensitive the receiver. Therefore, the minimum signal we can detect is a million times smaller at radio frequencies than at light frequencies. This is the same as saying that the sensitivity of a receiver at radio frequencies may be a million times better than at light frequencies. Radio frequencies, then, are still the most useful in the transmission and reception of messages, and probably will be for some time to come.

How can an interstellar message be recognized? After all, radio power from space is received all the time; this problem is the subject of study by radio astronomers night and day. The method of distinguishing intelligent signals from the radio waves generated by galaxies and gas clouds in space is fairly easy. The natural radio power of space is noise, which comes in at all frequencies and with the same strength at all times. Intelligent signals are concentrated in very narrow bands of frequencies, as described earlier, in order to get maximum range by eliminating as much receiver and space noise as possible. Moreover, the intensity of intelligent signals changes in pattern because of the information carried by them. It will be easy, then, to separate the intelligent from the natural signals. A special receiver can be built for the space search that responds only to power arriving in narrow bands of frequencies, and that will be sensitive to changes in signal strength.

There is one other type of interfering radio power our telescope should disregard: intelligent signals from the earth that are accidentally picked up by the telescope. This is one of the great problems faced by the astronomers using radio telescopes; the instruments always pick up, though weakly, any man-made signals that may be within their range.

It is necessary to have a way of telling easily if a signal has come from space, and this can be done. The point in space from which the signals are transmitted will stay fixed among the stars. This means that the sending point will seem to move across the sky as the earth turns. Signals from the earth, on the other hand, will always seem to come from the same direction. What is necessary, then, is a radio telescope that can be pointed in different directions, so that we can see if a signal originates in space or on the earth. Of course, such a telescope is necessary anyway, so that it can be kept pointed on the target stars.

Men know now that the messages of space are best collected by radio telescopes, and they know how to recognize a real message. Other communicative civilizations should have this information, too. The next step is to strike up a conversation.

CHAPTER SEVEN

The Search Begins

HIDDEN within the vast spaces of the Milky Way are over a billion targets for the search for intelligent life. With each target is a very large number of radio frequencies that might be carrying the signal meaning "We are here." There are not enough radio telescopes or years to explore all the frequencies while looking at all the possible targets. A decision has to be made as to which stars should be the first objects of this search, and which frequencies.

In earlier chapters it was noted that only stars not

much different from the sun are likely to support intelligent creatures. So the search should concentrate on them, and on the nearest of these stars first, since the inverse square law indicates that signals from the closest stars would be the strongest received on the earth. The two nearest such stars visible from the United States are the stars Tau Ceti, in the constellation of Cetus, the Whale, and the star Epsilon Eridani, in the constellation of Eridanus, the River. Both are about 10 light-years away. The chances of finding a civilization very close to the earth are small, so the first stars looked at may prove disappointing, but the search should keep moving out slowly into space. If the suppositions are correct, someday, before targets more than a thousand light-years away are searched, the message should be received.

There is still a question to be answered: At what frequencies shall we search? Many frequencies can be eliminated immediately. Above a certain frequency, about 10 thousand million cycles per second, the air of the earth is no longer transparent, no signals can get through; there is no value in searching at higher frequencies from the surface of the earth. As frequencies descend lower and lower, the natural radio noise coming from the Milky Way becomes increasingly stronger, making it harder to distinguish the signals from the noise. Any advanced civilization, will avoid these lower frequencies at which the galaxy "jams" the radio receivers. Astronomers on the earth avoid them now. The interstellar messages will not be arriving on those frequencies and there is no point in searching for them there. This leaves a special range, between about one thousand million and 10 thousand million cycles per second, that should be probed. This is still a tremendous number of frequencies and perhaps all will have to be tried.

Operating in ignorance and without direction like this is similar to trying to meet a friend in New York City without making arrangements in advance about a meeting place. One does not just wander the streets, looking everywhere. Instead, the most likely places to look are the places that are already familiar: Grand Central Station, for instance, or the newsstand at Times Square. There are similar places in every city with which most people are acquainted. This is what the astronomers in this search of space need: a Grand Central Station of the galaxy, some special frequency about which everyone in the Milky Way would know.

There is such a frequency. It is the frequency at which the hydrogen clouds floating among the stars send out radio waves. Hydrogen, as discussed earlier, is the basic building block of our galaxy. There is still a great deal of it left, and it continuously radiates on the radio frequency of 1,420,405,000 cycles per second. The study of this emanation of hydrogen is one of the most important subjects of astronomy, and a similar importance is almost certain in all civilizations that have discovered radio astronomy. There is only this one strong natural radio emission in space.

The search should begin, therefore, at frequencies very nearly the same as the hydrogen frequency. If this is not successful, other frequencies related to the hydrogen frequency should be tried. After all, hydrogen does make a good deal of noise at its own frequency, which would tend to mask signals. Signals at perhaps one-half or double the hydrogen frequency would be safe from this interference, but still use the hydrogen frequency as a guide.

If this search does not work, all the other frequencies should be tried, because it may be that another civilization has grown tired of waiting for interstellar communication and has gone on about its business. Other civilizations may not be purposely sending out signals at the hydrogen frequency to attract the attention of intelligent beings, but may be busily using radio at other frequencies for their own affairs. These private messages of theirs can still be found and would be evidence for the existence of communicative civilizations in space.

Man is ready to begin his search; and he has. In the spring of 1960, one morning before sunrise, a new radio receiver was hooked to the large 85-foot Howard E. Tatel radio telescope at the National Radio Astronomy Observatory in West Virginia. This receiver was

The Howard E. Tatel radio telescope.

constructed so that it would reject everything but intelligent signals from outer space. It used a parametric amplifier (shown in the upper right-hand corner) to get high sensitivity, and a tape recorder ran continuously to record any signals that might be received. The telescope was pointed at the first of the target stars. The receiver was turned on, and for the first time in history, mankind began to search seriously for a signal from another civilization.

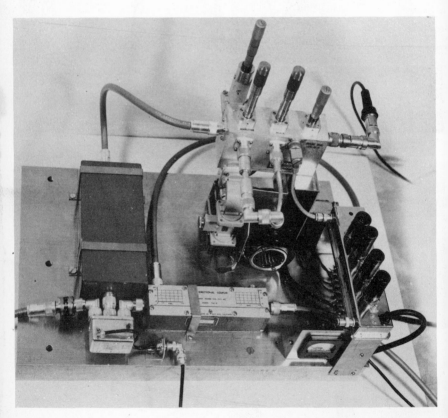

The first portion of the radio receiver used in Project Ozma (see Page 106).

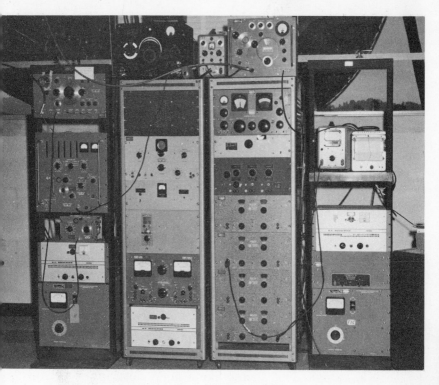

The remainder of the receiver used in Project Ozma.

Each morning, beginning at 3 A.M., the telescope was pointed at Tau Ceti and some new frequencies explored. The equipment shown above was used to determine accurately the frequency at which the observations were being made. When Tau Ceti set behind the mountains to the west, the telescope was swung to Epsilon Eridani, and the search carried on. After two months it was necessary to return the very expensive radio antenna to programs of ordinary radio-astronomy research, but by that time, the whole band around the hydrogen-line frequency had been explored. A signal was picked up twice, the same signal each time. This discovery was exciting, but moving the antenna showed that these were actually signals from the earth and not from space. When the two months were over, no evidence of signals coming from either star could be found in the records.

These were the first steps of the endeavor, at the National Radio Astronomy Observatory, named Project Ozma, a project that hopes to find signals from other intelligent beings. The project is named after the Princess of Oz, which, as you may remember from reading the popular "Oz" books, is a mythical land far away, difficult to reach, populated by strange and exotic beings. This seems like a good description of the place mankind is searching for. Also, the land of Oz is a land of childhood, and as we saw earlier, man is only now emerging from his childhood and preparing to take a place among the community of galactic civilizations that may exist.

It is clear that we should not be disappointed or discouraged because the first attempts of Project Ozma did not find another civilization. There was not time to examine nearly enough stars. It will take many more long years of work, with larger telescopes and faster and more sensitive receivers, to give a good

*The 140-foot telescope under construction
at the National Radio Astronomy Observatory.*

chance of success. At this time a new 140-foot telescope is under construction at the National Radio Astronomy Observatory that will be very suitable for use in the search for extraterrestrial signals. A 600-foot telescope may be built by the United States Navy at Sugar Grove, West Virginia. This enormous telescope would probably be the largest of its kind to be built for many years to come. Through projects like these, man will someday make the great effort required to meet the challenge, and he will succeed.

After another civilization is found, what then? If the star is very far away, two-way conversations will go very slowly indeed. The answer to a question will arrive only after a time equal to twice the distance to the star in light-years. Nevertheless man could undoubtedly learn much just by studying the transmissions sent out continually by the other civilization. Perhaps some of them will be designed to show what this other civilized planet is like; then this information would be available without any delay and without any question having to be asked.

When another civilization is found, a common language will have to be established with it. This is no easy task across thousands of light-years. For years archaeologists worked, trying unsuccessfully to decipher the hieroglyphics used by the Egyptians as writing. They didn't succeed until a piece of rock was found that had the same message inscribed on it in

*The 600-foot telescope projected by
the United States Navy at Sugar Grove, West Virginia.*

three languages: Greek and Egyptian hieroglyphics, as well as Archaic Greek. This was the famous Rosetta Stone, and it was the long-awaited key to the decipherment of these hieroglyphics. This was possible, of course, because the same message was described in a language that was known, as well as an unknown one. Perhaps there is a Rosetta Stone of space that will allow us to understand the language of another civilization. Mankind has in common with all civilizations in the Milky Way the universal laws of physics and mathematics, and the arrangement of the Milky Way itself. Perhaps these will serve the purpose.

If not, communicating civilizations can teach a language to one another in the same way a child learns to talk: by pointing to an object and saying its name. Probably the easiest way to point to an object would be to send a television picture of it. This would be slow, but any civilization would immediately recognize a television transmission and discover how to get the picture from it. Television transmissions have certain characteristics that make them easy to recognize.

What will be learned from contacting other civilizations? This is very hard to know, but there will certainly be many unexpected, surprising things among the interstellar messages. There will be many scientific and practical things, of course, but more important in the long run will be a knowledge of the many ways in which other intelligent beings utilize their intellects for practical and philosophical pursuits and the cultivation of beauty. The ways of man on the earth are probably only a few of all that have been used. Most important of all, man may learn more about his true position and importance in the universe, a question that has haunted all men almost from the time they could think, and still fascinates mankind today.

At this very minute, with almost absolute certainty, radio waves sent forth by other intelligent civilizations are falling on the earth. A telescope can be built that, pointed in the right place, and tuned to the right frequency, could discover these waves. Someday, from somewhere out among the stars, will come the answers to many of the oldest, most important, and most exciting questions mankind has asked.

Glossary

Amino Acids: Organic chemicals (see p. 116) based on the ammonia molecule, thus containing nitrogen. Many of them are the basic building blocks of the proteins.

Ammonia: A compound in which the molecule consists of three hydrogen atoms attached to one nitrogen atom.

Antenna: A device that converts electromagnetic radiation to electrical energy or the electrical energy to radiation. The antenna often is designed to concentrate the radiated power in a preferred direction when used to transmit power. When used to receive electromagnetic waves, the antenna often is designed to absorb as completely as possible the power coming from some directions, but to reject power coming from other sources. A radio telescope is usually one of these latter antennas.

Cepheid Variable: A type of variable star, not a double star, whose light pulsates regularly, following a certain fixed pattern. These variables are named after the constellation Cepheus in the northern sky where the first of this type was observed.

Cosmic Year: About 200 million years. Roughly, the time it takes for a star to complete an orbit around the center of our galactic system.

Doppler Effect: The apparent change in the frequency and wavelength of waves from a given source because of the motion of either the transmitter or receiver of the waves.

Electromagnetic Waves: Vibrations of both magnetic and electric fields, which travel through a vacuum at the speed of light. Both ordinary light and radio waves are forms of electromagnetic radiation, the

[114]

difference being that the length of light waves is about 20 millionths of an inch, while the length of radio waves may be between approximately one inch and many miles.

Galaxy: A large system of gas, dust, and as many as a million million stars, all held together by the gravitational pull of the objects on one another. Visually, they appear principally as nearly spherical bodies or flat bodies containing spiral arms.

Inverse Square Law: A law of physics stating that electromagnetic waves traveling freely through space become less intense in proportion to the square of the distance over which they have traveled.

Laser: A device using the special properties of some crystals, such as the ruby, to generate powerful light beams limited to a very narrow range of frequencies. The light is radiated in such a manner that it may be very effectively focused to a point, or transmitted in a narrow beam.

Maser: A device using the special properties of certain crystals, such as the ruby, at very low temperatures and in a magnetic field, to amplify radio signals. A maser usually adds much less unwanted noise than other amplifiers, and thus enables the construction of receiving systems of better than normal sensitivity.

Milky Way: The large spiral galaxy of which our solar system is a member. The familiar Milky Way of the night sky is the disk of this galaxy as seen from the earth.

Nova: The explosion of a star, probably an old one, in which the star throws off some of its material and becomes as much as 50 thousand times brighter for a period of about a month.

Nucleic Acids: Organic acids composed of very large molecules that act as the blueprints, or controls, in the production of new living materials.

Organic Chemicals: A compound based on the carbon atom. Because of the ability of carbon to join with itself in long chains of carbon atoms, many organic molecules are very large and complicated, permitting the production of numerous compounds having a wide range of properties. Oil, plastics, and living organisms are all made of these compounds.

Parametric Amplifier: A device using the characteristics of certain crystals to give amplification of radio waves. The noise added to the signals by the amplifier is much less than with the average radio receiver, allowing very high sensitivity to be achieved. This device operates well at normal room temperature.

Photoelectric Cell: A device that converts light energy into electrical energy.

Planetary Nebula: A cloud of gas thrown off by an old star, and caused to fluoresce by ultraviolet light emitted by the star.

Proteins: Compounds containing very large organic molecules composed primarily of amino acids. Proteins are the primary constituents of many portions of living things, such as muscle and skin. They are essential to the process of converting food to new living material.

Spectrograph: A device that separates the light from a star according to wavelength, or color, and records the amount of light found at each wavelength. The result is called a spectrum. The wavelengths at which light is missing reveal the elements present in a star.

Supernova: A much more violent explosion than a nova, in which a great deal of material is thrown off, and the star becomes perhaps 100 million times brighter for a month or more.

21-cm Line: The spectral line emitted by hydrogen atoms at a wavelength of about 21 centimeters, the exact wavelength received being determined by the Doppler effect due to motion of the radiating atoms.

Ultraviolet Light: Light at wavelengths slightly shorter than the violet, which are the shortest wavelengths the human eye can detect.

White Dwarf: A small star, emitting only a feeble light, in which material is very tightly packed together. A cubic inch of material may weigh a ton. It is the final state of an old star.

Suggestions for Further Reading

Gatland, Kenneth and Dempster, Derek, *Inhabited Universe*. New York: Fawcett Publications ("Premier Books," paperback), 1959. A comprehensive book for the general reader, dealing with the chemical and physical nature of the earth and the planets, and speculating on the future evolution of man and life on other worlds.

Heuer, Kenneth, *Men of Other Planets*. New York: Viking Press, Inc., 1951. An easy-to-read discussion by a former Hayden Planetarium astronomer. Speculation about life on other worlds, based on the latest scientific discoveries.

Jones, Sir Harold Spencer, *Life on Other Worlds*. New York: The Macmillan Co. (2nd revised ed.), 1954. New York: New American Library of World Literature, Inc. ("Mentor Books," paperback), 1956. A readable survey by England's former Astronomer Royal, covering the conditions necessary for terrestrial life and the physical properties of the planets; one chapter on the possibility of life in other planetary systems.

Nourse, Alan E., *Nine Planets*. New York: Pyramid Books, 1960. A book for the general reader by a physician with a long-standing interest in the subject. What men may expect to find when they explore the planets; the possibility of life and the forms of life that may exist.

Ovenden, Michael W., *Life in the Universe*. Garden City, L.I.: Doubleday & Company, Inc. ("Anchor Books," paperback), 1962. A semipopular book written by an astronomer, dealing with the nature, adaptability, and evolution of life on the earth, and the types of life that may exist on other planets.

Strughold, Hubertus, *The Green and Red Planet*.

Albuquerque, New Mexico: University of New Mexico Press, 1953. A physiological study of the possibility of life on Mars for the general reader. Covers
such subjects as the methods of biological study, the
foundations of life as we know it, and Mars as a biological environment.

Index

ACKNOWLEDGMENTS

The author would like to extend his appreciation for permission to use the photographs and diagrams reproduced in this book to: the American Museum–Hayden Planetarium, New York, New York, for the pictures on pages 14, 22 46, 50, 51 and 69; Bell Telephone Laboratories, Inc., New York, New York, for the pictures on pages 87, 90, 91, and 93; Mount Wilson and Palomar Observatories, Mount Palomar California, for the Frontispiece and the photographs on pages 17, 18, 20, 24, 28, 29, 30, 31, 33, 37, 38, 39, 41, 52, 53, 54, and 55; the National Radio Astronomy Observatory, Green Bank, West Virginia for the pictures on pages 85, 95, 103, 104, 105, and 107; the University of Oregon for the pictures on pages 62 and 63 used by permission of the Condon Lectures Committee, Oregon State System of Higher Education, from the monograph "Chemical Evolution" by Melvin Calvin (Figs. 7 and 8); and the United States Naval Radio Research Station at Sugar Grove, West Virginia, for the picture on page 109.

ABOUT THE AUTHOR

Dr. Frank D. Drake is an associate astronomer at the National Radio Astronomy Observatory in Green Bank, West Virginia, where he has been directing Project Ozma.

Born in Chicago, he received a Bachelor of Engineering Physics form Cornell University, and a Ph.D. in astronomy from Harvard University. In 1955, after serving as an electronics officer in the Navy, he went to Harvard, where he was associated with the Agassiz Station Radio Astronomy Project. In 1958 he was Director of the Astronomical Research Group of the Ewen Knight Corporation, East Natick, Massachusetts, where he participated in the development of radio sextants and other radio astronomy equipment. Formerly head of Project Ozma, Dr. Drake is presently Head of the Scientific Services Division of the National Radio Astronomy Observatory.

[128]